Streams in the Desert

Lives God Touched in the Desert

J. MICHAEL LESTER

First published in 2005 by *Striving Together Publications*, a ministry of Lancaster Baptist Church, Lancaster, CA 93535.
Striving Together Publications is committed to providing tried, trusted, and proven books that will further equip local churches to carry out the Great Commission. Your comments and suggestions are valued.

Striving Together Publications
4020 E. Lancaster Blvd.
Lancaster, CA 93535
800.201.7748

Cover design by Craig Parker and Stephen Houk

Layout by Craig Parker

Editing, proofreading, and assistance by
Esther Brown, Amanda Michael, and Kayla Nelson

ISBN 0-9726506-9-5

Printed in the United States of America

Table of Contents

LESSON ONE

Here Comes the Dreamer

Genesis 37:1–23

Memory Verse

"Where there is no vision, the people perish: but he that keepeth the law, happy is he."—Proverbs 29:18

Introduction

The life of Joseph reveals many types of the Lord Jesus Christ. This lesson focuses on the dreams that he had as a teen and the thirteen years of difficulty before his dreams became a reality. This lesson reveals to us the providence of God; we are never out of His care.

Lesson Theme

Learning the principle of God's providence

Introduction

____

____

____

I. Big ____________! Big ____________!

A. Joseph's dreams involved Leadership

B. Joseph's dreams ____________________ of his brothers

II. Big ____________! Big ____________!

A. An ____________ son does ____________

"Let every soul be subject unto the higher powers. For there is no power but of God: the powers that be are ordained of God. Whosoever therefore resisteth the power, resisteth the ordinance of God: and they that resist shall receive to themselves damnation. For rulers are not a terror to good works, but to the evil. Wilt thou then not be afraid of the power? do that which is good, and thou shalt have praise of the same."—ROMANS 13:1–3

B. The root of ________________ springs up

"Looking diligently lest any man fail of the grace of God; lest any root of bitterness springing up trouble you, and thereby many be defiled."—HEBREWS 12:15

III. Big ____________! Big ____________!

A. ________________ by Potiphar

B. Cast from Potiphar's _______ to the _______

C. Taken from ____________ to ____________

D. ___________ by Pharaoh to the ___________

E. ________________ by the ______________

"...Me have ye bereaved of my children: Joseph is not, and Simeon is not, and ye will take Benjamin away: all these things are against me...My son shall not go down with you; for his brother is dead...if mischief befall him by the way in which ye go, then shall ye bring down my gray hairs with sorrow to the grave..."
—Genesis 42:36, 38

F. Given a ____________________

Conclusion

____

____

____

Study Questions

1. Why did Jacob love Joseph more than his brothers?

2. Why did the brothers hate Joseph?

3. What were the objects in Joseph's two dreams?

4. How did Joseph's brothers respond to his dreams? How did Jacob respond to Joseph's dreams?

5. Where were the brothers supposed to be feeding the flocks? Where were they actually at?

6. What was the original game plan for disposing of Joseph? How did Reuben's suggestion change it?

7. List four or five dreams that you have for your life.

8. List an area in the past week where you did "just enough" and not the whole job.

9. What thoughts were going through Joseph's mind while sitting in that well?

Prayer

Write out a prayer expressing to God some of your dreams and the realization that to get to those dreams some time of desert experience may be necessary.

LESSON TWO

Three Days into the Desert

Exodus 2:23–25

Memory Verse

"*I will worship toward thy holy temple, and praise thy name for thy lovingkindness and for thy truth: for thou hast magnified thy word above all thy name.*"—Psalm 138:2

Introduction

The children of Israel had been in Egypt for 400 years. Perhaps they thought that they had been forgotten, or perhaps they had even forgotten how to worship. The God of Abraham, Isaac, and Jacob was preparing to appear to them. He wanted to be their personal God as well. They could not worship Him in Egypt, for that was a type of the world. Worship involves separation. God was preparing these people to learn how to give praise in the desert.

Lesson Theme

Learning the principle of praise

Introduction

____

____

____

I. The Pleas to God

"*We want to be* free *to* worship."

A. God Sees the need

"*...I have surely seen the affliction of my people which are in Egypt, and have heard their cry by reason of their taskmasters...Now therefore, behold, the cry of the children of Israel is come unto me: and I have also seen the oppression....*"—EXODUS 3:7

B. God Prepares a Man

II. The Demand of Pharaoh

"*Let's* make a deal."

"*Let my people go, that they may hold a feast unto me in the wilderness...Let us go...three days' journey into the desert, and sacrifice unto the LORD....*"—EXODUS 5:1, 3

***A. The* demand *is made to* compromise**

***B. There is no room for* compromise *when* the Lord has spoken**

III. The Provision in the Desert

"*Stand still and watch the LORD work.*"

A. *The* Prayers *of the Jews are answered—* sort of*!*

B. *It is the* Lord's battle

Conclusion

____

____

____

Study Questions

1. List the ten plagues that God brought upon Egypt (you must look back in chapter 7 for the first one).

2. Which plague could the magicians of Egypt no longer imitate?

3. What were the families supposed to do in preparation for the night of Passover?

4. What actions were Moses and the Israelites to take at the brink of the Red Sea?

5. List some qualities of praise given to God in chapter 15.

6. The Israelites thought they were in the desert of life even though they were in the midst of a miracle. What are some desert experiences you are facing right now that could turn into a miracle?

7. The Israelites complained as they were being led by God. What have you complained about today?

8. What are you allowing the Pharaohs of your life to compromise? Bible reading, prayer, convictions, church services, giving?

Prayer

Write out a prayer of praise reflecting God's qualities and His work in your life.

LESSON THREE

There Came a Messenger

1 Samuel 23

Memory Verse

"For all this I considered in my heart even to declare all this, that the righteous, and the wise, and their works, are in the hand of God..."—Ecclesiastes 9:1

Introduction

When you study the life of someone who is after God's own heart, you cannot help but learn valuable truths. In this lesson, a leader is taking a stand for righteousness. He is used greatly of the Lord to deliver a city, which in turn prepares to turn him over to Saul! After hazarding his own life, the gratitude of the city is shown by betrayal. Immediately, David must go back "on the run." While running for his life, he will learn that there is a God in Heaven who watches over the affairs of man. His trust in the Lord will be greatly increased, and he will be greater prepared to lead Israel as king one day.

Lesson Theme

Learning the principle of protection

Introduction

I. David is Faithful to the Will of God

"And every one that was in distress, and every one that was in debt, and every one that was discontented, gathered themselves unto him…"—1 SAMUEL 22:2

A. David's love for Israel

B. David's love for the will of God

II. David is Forsaken by Those He Helped

A. King Saul learns *where David is* located

B. David needs a word *from the* Lord

"Thy word is a lamp unto my feet, and a light unto my path."—PSALM 119:105

"Fear not: for the hand of Saul my father shall not find thee; and thou shalt be king over Israel…"
—1 SAMUEL 23:17

III. God Has Never forgotten David

A. The Protection *of David by* God

B. The providence *of God in David's* Life

Conclusion

___

___

___

Study Questions

1. What were the Philistines trying to get from Keilah?

2. When faced with whether or not to fight for Keilah, what action did David take first?

3. Who came to see David while in the woods and what message did he bring?

4. Why did Saul stop pursuing David?

5. David cared for God's people and took responsibility for them. Who do you need to help take responsibility for?

6. List some insecurities you have. Realize that insecurities do not show you that you are out of God's perfect will. David was in God's perfect will, yet he was very insecure!

7. Who have you helped rescue and then had turn and hurt you?

8. What message has God sent you lately? Remember it can come through your enemy.

Prayer

Write out a prayer to God telling Him your desert experience and sharing with Him that you want Him to make these trials that you are enduring a step of growth in your life.

LESSON FOUR

Just a Voice

John 1

Memory Verse

"But ye shall receive power, after that the Holy Ghost is come upon you: and ye shall be witnesses unto me both in Jerusalem, and in all Judaea, and in Samaria, and unto the uttermost part of the earth."—Acts 1:8

Introduction

People will often use the excuse, "I would do that, but I am just a ____________." John could have used that excuse as well, but instead he determined to be "just a voice" for the Lamb of God. Consequently, God blessed the ministry of this man and paid him a high compliment: "There is no greater prophet born of women than John the Baptist!" The truth is simply that God can use anyone who will be yielded unto Him.

Lesson Theme

Learning the principle of spiritual power

Introduction

____

____

____

I. The Context of His Life

A. *The birth of John* Fulfilled Prophecy

B. *John* Grew *in* Privacy

II. The Characteristics of His Life

A. Courageous

"In God I will praise his word, in God I have put my trust; I will not fear what flesh can do unto me."
—Psalm 56:4

B. Zealous

C. Holy

"According as he hath chosen us in him before the foundation of the world, that we should be holy and without blame before him in love:"—Ephesians 1:4

D. Common

"This is the Lord's doing; it is marvellous in our eyes."
—Psalm 118:23

III. The Calling on His Life

A. To be a voice

B. To point people to The Lamb of God

Conclusion

____

____

____

Study Questions

1. Why was John sent?

2. Who did John himself claim to be?

3. How did John explain that Christ was greater than himself?

4. What did John call Jesus?

5. What is God's purpose for your life?

6. Where was John trained for his purpose? Where is God training you?

7. John was to make His path straight. John was very sensitive to sin. What sin bothered you today?

8. How can you be bold like John when you enter work, a restaurant, or an airport this week?

Prayer

Write a prayer to God expressing His purpose for your life and asking Him to give you boldness and a sensitivity to sin like John had.

LESSON FIVE

The Temptation of Christ

Matthew 4:1–11

Memory Verse

"Thy word have I hid in mine heart, that I might not sin against thee."—Psalm 119:11

Introduction

Have you ever been guilty of using the phrase "the Devil made me do it"? The narrative given to us in Matthew 4 shows us that the Wicked One has no power over the Word of God. It alone is our sword (Ephesians 6:12). The sword is both an offensive and a defensive weapon. We use the Word of God for our protection as well as for the advancement of the cause of Christ. The wilderness would provide a great backdrop to showcase the power of the Word of God against the wiles of the Devil.

Lesson Theme

Learning the principle of God's precepts

Introduction

____

____

____

I. The Word of God ____________

"Great peace have they which love thy law: and nothing shall offend them."—Psalm 119:165

A. *Peace for* ____________________

B. *Peace to* ____________________

II. The Word of God ____________

A. *God's Word helps us deal with* ____________________

B. *God's Word helps us deal with* ____________________

C. *God's Word helps us deal with* ____________________

III. The Word of God ____________

A. *The Word of God penetrates the hearts of* ____________________

B. The Word of God penetrates the hearts of

____

"Wherewithal shall a young man cleanse his way? by taking heed thereto according to thy word."
—Psalm 119:9

B. The Word of God penetrates the heart of

____

Conclusion

____

____

____

Study Questions

1. Who led Jesus into the wilderness?

2. How many verses did Jesus use to defeat Satan?

3. What did the first temptation deal with?

4. What did the second temptation deal with?

5. What did the third temptation deal with?

6. What two things does this passage show about Christ?

7. What is a sin of the flesh that you struggle with? Find a verse to memorize to defeat that sin.

8. Everyone struggles with pride. Think of some specific instances when you must watch your pride. Pick and memorize a verse to use as defense.

Prayer

Write out a prayer thanking God for the power of His Word and ask Him to help you hide it in your heart.

LESSON SIX

The Preparation of a Leader

Exodus 1–4

Memory Verse

"For the law was given by Moses, but grace and truth came by Jesus Christ."—John 1:17

Introduction

Perhaps no other Old Testament character needs less of an introduction than Moses. His life neatly divides into three separate forty year periods. His first forty years, we find him as a prince of Egypt. His second forty years, we see a prince that has left the palace for the desert. Of course, his last forty years he is pictured as the leader of the Israelites. The focus of this lesson deals with those wilderness years where God takes a man trained in the worldly ways of leadership and gives him a biblical view. It is during these preparatory years when Moses will marry and receive his calling into the "ministry."

Lesson Theme

Learning the principle of preparation

Introduction

____

____

____

I. The Man Must Be Broken

A. Brute strength ***cannot deliver a nation***

"Some trust in chariots, and some in horses: but we will remember the name of the LORD our God."
—Psalm 20:7

"With him is an arm of flesh; but with us is the LORD our God to help us, and to fight our battles. And the people rested themselves upon the words of Hezekiah king of Judah."—2 Chronicles 32:8

"There is no king saved by the multitude of an host: a mighty man is not delivered by much strength."
—Psalm 33:16

"For I will not trust in my bow, neither shall my sword save me."—Psalm 44:6

B. Broken Men ***can be rebuilt and used again***

II. God Uses Battles In Our Preparation

A. ***Moses*** Returns ***to*** Egypt

B. ***Moses*** comforts Israel

C. ***Moses*** faces Pharaoh

III. God Gives Boldness to His Servants

A. God-confidence ***is better than*** Self-confidence

B. ***God is no*** Respecter of persons

Conclusion

____

____

____

Study Questions

1. Briefly outline the story of Moses' birth and raising.

2. Who did Moses kill and why?

3. What were the names of Moses' wife, father-in-law, and son?

4. What was Moses to call God when addressing the people of Israel?

5. What two signs did God give to Moses?

6. Just imagine for a minute. What kind of life did Moses have while living in the palace of the greatest man on earth?

7. What desert experience has God taken you through to break you?

8. List some emotions that would have been going through Moses' mind as he prepared to stand before Pharaoh.

Prayer

Write out a prayer asking God to keep you broken so He can have victories through you instead of you doing it on your own and messing everything up.

LESSON SEVEN

Feeding the Multitudes

Matthew 14:13–21

Memory Verse

"Yea, they spake against God; they said, Can God furnish a table in the wilderness? Behold, he smote the rock, that the waters gushed out, and the streams overflowed; can he give bread also? can he provide flesh for his people?"
—Psalm 78:19–20

Introduction

The theme of God's provision runs throughout the Bible. Elijah is fed by a raven; Daniel is protected in a den of lions; the Hebrew children are spared from the fire; the disciples were taught to pray for daily provision, etc. In Matthew 14 (parallel John 6), the disciples would soon learn that man's extremities are God's opportunities. They learn in this desert place that the Living Water makes streams in the desert. The application is so timely: Do we really believe that God is able to meet all of our needs? We know that He can handle all of eternity for us, but how about the things we need here on earth? If we can trust God enough to provide us with salvation, we can trust Him enough to provide for all of our temporary needs.

Lesson Theme

Learning the principle of provision

Introduction

____

____

____

I. The ______________ of ______________
—A ______________________________

A. The ______________ of John

B. The ______________ for ______________

II. The ______________ of ______________
—A ______________________________

A. The ______________ of the ______________

B. The ______________ of the ______________

"Take heed to the ministry which thou hast received in the Lord, that thou fulfil it."—COLOSSIANS 4:17

"…and that they have addicted themselves to the ministry of the saints."—1 CORINTHIANS 16:15

III. The Provision of the Saviour —A Blessed Supply

A. Everything is done decently *and in* order

B. The food is blessed, broken distributed

C. Is it finally Over*?*

Conclusion

"The God of my rock; in him will I trust: he is my shield, and the horn of my salvation, my high tower, and my refuge, my saviour; thou savest me from violence."—2 SAMUEL 22:3

"Trust ye in the LORD for ever: for in the LORD JEHOVAH is everlasting strength:"—ISAIAH 26:4

____

____

____

Study Questions

1. Why did Jesus take His disciples to a "desert place"?

2. Why was the multitude following Jesus?

3. List some lessons that you think Jesus was trying to teach to the disciples on this particular day.

4. Jesus and His disciples were obviously very busy, but why did Jesus take time to feed the multitude instead of just sending them home?

5. In the business of your own life, what are some things you are putting aside that you think the Lord would want you to do in order to provide for the needs of others?

6. The feeding of the multitude was done "decently and in order." Write down one thing in your life that should be more organized in order for you to be more effective for Jesus Christ, and list several things you can do to improve in this area.

7. What is it that you need God to provide in your own life?

8. How have you seen God provide in the past?

Prayer

Write out a prayer to God applying the principles you've learned in this passage.

LESSON EIGHT

New Life in the Desert

Acts 8

Memory Verse

"The Lord is not slack concerning his promise, as some men count slackness; but is longsuffering to us-ward, not willing that any should perish, but that all should come to repentance."—2 Peter 3:9

Introduction

The story of the conversion of the Ethiopian eunuch is amazing. Every minute detail is orchestrated by a Heavenly Father who is concerned that *"not...any should perish, but...come to repentance."* God is not One that arbitrarily wills people to Hell. On the contrary, we find in Scripture a picture of a God Who is love. He *"so loved the world"* that He provided a *"propitiation for...the sins of the world."* In this chapter, you will see an evangelist that is involved in a great "spiritual revival" in Samaria. The heart and desire of this evangelist would be to stay in this city where God is moving for a long time. At the height of these meetings, God calls this servant to the desert! Why? Because God is just as concerned about the one "lost lamb" as the multitudes in the city.

Lesson Theme

Learning the principle of God's plan

Introduction

____

____

____

I. The ___Call___ of God to ___Philip___

A. It was a ___Call___ to the ___desert___

B. It was an ___immediate___ and ___Enthusiastic___ response

II. The ___Concern___ of God for ___People___

A. One ___Soul___ matters to God

B. One ___soul___ makes a difference

III. The ___Conversion___ of one ___Person___

A. The ___Gosple___ is the power of God unto ___Salvation___

B. ___Baptism___ is not part of the Gospel

Conclusion

Study Questions

1. What four words describe Philip's response to God's command to him? What kind of obedience was this?

2. Where was this soulwinning prospect from? Whom did he work for? What did he do for her?

3. Why had this eunuch come to Jerusalem?

4. Where was the eunuch reading from in the Scriptures?

5. What was the eunuch's statement in verse 37 that proved he had accepted Christ and was ready for baptism?

6. After Philip was caught away, what adverb describes how the eunuch went on his way?

7. What request has God recently given you that you have had to respond to? Did you do it with immediate and enthusiastic obedience even though you did not understand the reason behind the request?

8. What are three Scriptural truths you see from God's concern in reaching this one man?

Prayer

Write out a prayer for a specific soul that needs to come to Christ for salvation.

LESSON NINE

First Things First

1 Kings 17

Memory Verse

"But seek ye first the kingdom of God, and his righteousness; and all these things shall be added unto you."—Matthew 6:33

Introduction

Elijah is an interesting character in the Old Testament. In 1 Kings 17, Elijah is going to challenge a widow to re-evaluate what is really important. This woman is resigned to cook some bread and then die. Her life has no purpose and the drought has brought a dark cloud of discouragement and doubt. The prophet of God comes on the scene and requests that she take care of him first. Is it really a legitimate request to put the work of God first? There are so many pressing needs; so many cumbersome burdens. It was a legitimate request then, and it still remains so today. God's people take care of God's work. When we put His work first, everything else falls into place. When we change the order to self first, God second—we find only heartache and dry, desert experiences.

Lesson Theme

Learning the principle of priorities

Introduction

____

____

____

I. Elijah's Unbelievable Request

A. He asks for WATER

B. He asks for bread

C. He asks to be served first

II. The Widow's Unbelievable Response

A. The widow demonstrates obedience
"If ye love me, keep my commandments."—John 14:15

B. The widow demonstrates trust

III. The Lords Unbelievable Resources

A. Her faith provides for her Future

B. ***Her faith provides for her*** house

C. ***Her faith provides for her*** posterity

Conclusion

____

____

____

Study Questions

1. Why was Elijah hiding?

2. Where was he hiding?

3. How was Elijah being provided for?

4. After the brook dried up, where did God tell Elijah to go?

5. Because this widow obeyed, what happened? Explain from verses 15–16.

6. According to this passage and many others, we are to put God's work first. Put yourself in this woman's shoes for a moment and write down some things that would be going through her mind.

7. What promise was this woman trusting in? What promise can you claim when you put God's work first?

8. This woman had an awesome story to tell her offspring! What story of God's provision do you have to tell?

Prayer

Write out a prayer of praise for God's provision for you as you put His work and man first.

LESSON TEN

Look and Live

Numbers 21:1–9

Memory Verse

"And as Moses lifted up the serpent in the wilderness, even so must the Son of man be lifted up."—John 3:14

Introduction

Most people are not fond of snakes. Imagine the horror of the Jews in Numbers 21 as the "fiery serpents" are causing death to abound. According to 1 Corinthians 10:9–10, these Jews were guilty of two sins: tempting God and murmuring against Him. The purpose of this lesson is to help us not to be guilty of these same grave errors.

Lesson Theme

Learning the principle of persuasion

Introduction

____

____

____

I. The ____________ of ______________

A. Difficulty is to be ________ on the ________

B. Focusing on ______________ instead of the __________ causes ______________

"And let us not be weary in well doing: for in due season we shall reap if we faint not."—Galatians 6:9

II. The ____________ Against __________

A. The nation speaks against God

B. The nation speaks against God's messenger

C. God does not excuse the complaints

III. The ____________ for ______________

A. The ____________ of God's ____________

B. The ____________ of the ______________

Conclusion

Study Questions

1. In verse 4, what word describes how the people were feeling? Why were they feeling this way?

2. What were the people's complaints?

3. How long did God wait after the people repented to send a remedy?

4. What happened when a person looked at the brazen serpent?

5. When was the last time you got discouraged?

6. Everyone gets discouraged, but to what extent did the people take their discouragement? Who did they speak out against?

7. Give three qualities of Moses as a leader in this passage.

8. Relate this story to soulwinning with Moses as the soulwinner, the brazen serpent as the Gospel, and the people as the sinners.

Prayer

Write out a prayer asking God to help you lift the Gospel high so that people can look and live.

LESSON ELEVEN

Responding to God

Genesis 22:1–19

Memory Verse

"And Samuel said, Hath the LORD as great delight in burnt offerings and sacrifices, as in obeying the voice of the LORD? Behold, to obey is better than sacrifice, and to hearken than the fat of rams."—1 Samuel 15:22

Introduction

God is always looking for people like those we read about in the Bible who will readily commit all to serve Him. The Word of God reveals God's searching for man and not man's searching for God. God seeks us out for salvation and for service. In this Old Testament chapter, we see some principles of how we are to respond when God is looking for us to serve. In short, He is looking for unquestioning obedience.

Lesson Theme

Learning the principle of patience

Introduction

____

____

____

I. The ____________________ to Abraham

A. *God asked for his ______________—not ______________, but ______________*

B. *God asked for his ___________—his ________*

C. *God asked for the _____________________ —his ________________________*

II. The ____________________ of Abraham

A. *It was ________________*

B. *It was ________________*

C. *It was ________________*

D. *It was ________________*

E. *It was ________________*

F. *It was ________________*

III. The ________________ for Abraham

A. He was ________________ of God

B. God ________________ His ___________

Conclusion

____

____

____

Study Questions

1. What kind of obedience did Abraham show?

2. What statement of faith is seen in verse 5?

3. What did God know about Abraham according to verse 12?

4. Does God place a higher value on sacrifice or obedience?

5. What is God asking from you?

6. Living by faith is obedience even when you cannot explain or reason it out. Do you have anything like this in your life now?

7. After God brings you through a "faith experience", do you have a time of worship? How?

8. What was Abraham's promise and reward for obedience?

Prayer

Write out a prayer asking God to increase your faith in Him—be specific.

LESSON TWELVE

What Doest Thou Here?

1 Kings 19:1–21

Memory Verse

"And let us not be weary in well doing: for in due season we shall reap, if we faint not."—Galatians 6:9

Introduction

Discouragement has caused many soldiers to drop out of this race. We find this trait even in the most dedicated Christians at times. Elijah has just experienced a great victory and he is now running to hide! He must learn that trials will only strengthen us if we remain steadfast to the end. It is always too early to quit!

Lesson Theme

Learning the principle of perseverance

Introduction

____

____

____

I. The ______________ of Perseverance

A. ______________ *comes after* ______________

B. *No one is* ______________ *from* ______________

"Elias was a man subject to like passions as we are, and he prayed earnestly that it might not rain: and it rained not on the earth by the space of three years and six months."—James 5:17

II. The ______________ of Perseverance

A. ______________________

"For God hath not given us the spirit of fear; but of power, and of love, and of a sound mind."
—2 Timothy 1:7

B. ______________________

"And let us not be weary in well doing: for in due season we shall reap, if we faint not."—Galatians 6:9

C. Failure

"For a just man falleth seven times, and riseth up again: but the wicked shall fall into mischief."
—Proverbs 24:16

III. The Focus of Perseverance

A. *Elijah went to the* Presence

"Looking unto Jesus the author and finisher of our faith; who for the joy that was set before him endured the cross, despising the shame, and is set down at the right hand of the throne of God."—Hebrews 12:2

B. *Elisha was anointed* after *this* discouragement

Conclusion

Study Questions

1. What did Elijah ask God to do to him in verse 4?

2. List some things God provided for Elijah in the midst of his discouragement.

3. What mountain did Elijah go to?

4. Where was God found (verses 11–12)?

5. Who did God have ready to follow in Elijah's footsteps that needed mentoring?

6. The devil used his most powerful tool on Elijah here—what is it?

7. Testing comes after victory. Name an instance this has been true in your life.

8. List other Bible characters who thought about quitting.

Prayer

Write out a prayer asking God to help you set up some guidelines to keep you from the sin of discouragement.

LESSON THIRTEEN

Wrestling with an Angel

Genesis 32:1–30

Memory Verse

"And he spake a parable unto them to this end, that men ought always to pray, and not to faint."—Luke 18:1

Introduction

In this passage, we read of the famous account of Jacob wrestling with the angel all night long. As morning breaks, he realizes that he is in great need of God's blessings on his life. With dogged determination, he holds on as God reveals to him a new name—Israel. Jacob has the opportunity to shed the reputation of the "supplanter and deceiver." Now, he can be recognized as a prince with God. What made the difference in his life? The answer is simple: Time in prayer and communion with God changes everything!

Lesson Theme

Learning the principle of prayer

Introduction

____

____

____

I. The ______________ of Jacob

A. The __________ from __________

B. The __________ of __________

II. The ______________ of Jacob

A. He ______ as though it all depends on God

B. He ______ as though it is all left up to him

III. The __________ with the __________

A. Power in heavenly ______________ requires ______________

"Yea, he had power over the angel, and prevailed: he wept, and made supplication unto him: he found him in Bethel, and there he spake with us."—HOSEA 12:4

B. __________ with the Holy One changes us

Conclusion

Study Questions

1. Who did Jacob realize was protecting him in verses 1–2?

2. How many men did Esau have with him?

3. What brook did Jacob wrestle by?

4. What did the Angel change Jacob's name to?

5. What did Jacob call that place and why?

6. Stop and list some of God's mercies to you (verse 10).

7. Do you come up with your own plan to "help God out"? Give an example.

8. Have you ever wrestled with God until He sent you a blessing?

Prayer

Write out a prayer, giving any worry, fear, or question in your life to God.

For additional Christian
growth resources visit
www.strivingtogether.com